100 SOLOS
SAXOPHONE

Arranged by Robin De Smet.

GW00645531

1987

To Deanie
happy holiday
present love Hazel.

WISE PUBLICATIONS
LONDON/NEW YORK/SYDNEY/COLOGNE

EXCLUSIVE DISTRIBUTORS:
MUSIC SALES LIMITED
78 NEWMAN STREET, LONDON WIP 3LA, ENGLAND
MUSIC SALES PTY, LIMITED
27 CLARENDON STREET, ARTARMON, SYDNEY, NSW 2064, AUSTRALIA

BOOK DESIGN BY PEARCE MARCHBANK STUDIO
PRINTED IN ENGLAND BY THE CAMELOT PRESS LIMITED, SOUTHAMPTON

Sing.

Words and Music by Joe Raposo.

Strangers In The Night.

Music by Bert Kaempfert. Words by Charles Singleton & Eddie Snyder.

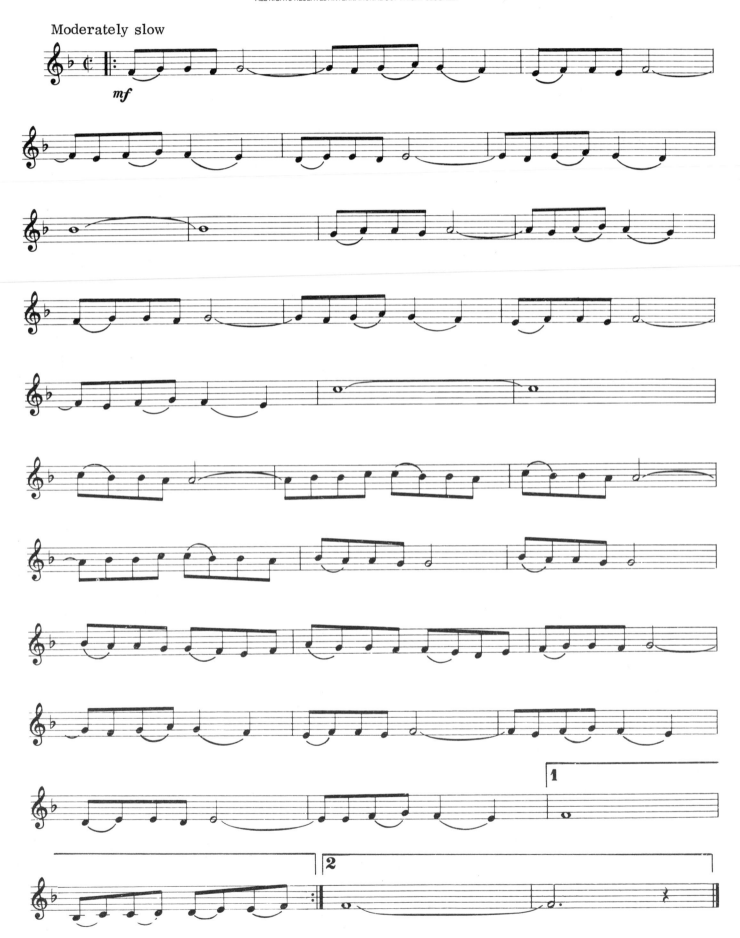

Truly Scrumptious.
Words and Music by Richard M. Sherman and Robert B. Sherman.

Broadly

Scarborough Fair
Traditional

Moderately slow

Smile.
Words by John Turner & Geoffrey Parsons. Music by Charles Chaplin.

Andante

Bye Bye Baby.

Words by Leo Robin. Music by Jule Styne.

A Dream

Tchaikovsky

Moderato

Romance
Beethoven

You're The Devil In Disguise.
Words and Music by Bill Giant, Bernie Baum and Florence Kaye.

Little Boxes.
Words and Music by Malvina Reynolds.

Moderate Waltz Tempo

Going To The Zoo.
Words and Music by Tom Paxton.

Brightly

Mary's Boy Child.
Words and Music by Jester Hairston.

Getting To Know You.
Words by Oscar Hammerstein II. Music by Richard Rodgers.

I Love You Because.

Words and Music by Leon Payne.

Who Do You Think You Are Kidding Mr. Hitler.
Words by Jimmy Perry. Music by Jimmy Perry & Derek Taverner.

From Russia With Love.
Words and Music by Lionel Bart.

Moderato

Chim Chim Cher-ee.
Words and Music by Richard M. Sherman & Robert B. Sherman.

Blue Moon.
Words by Lorenz Hart. Music by Richard Rodgers.

Morning Has Broken

Traditional

Moderato

Jolene.
Words and Music by Dolly Parton.

Serenade
Schubert

Moderato

Minuet

Handel

Moderato

The Green Leaves Of Summer.
Words by Paul Francis Webster. Music by Dimitri Tiomkin.

Laura.
Words by Johnny Mercer. Music by David Raksin.

Slowly, with expression

Days Of Wine And Roses.

Words by Johnny Mercer. Music by Henry Mancini.

As Long As He Needs Me.
Words and Music by Lionel Bart.

Moderato

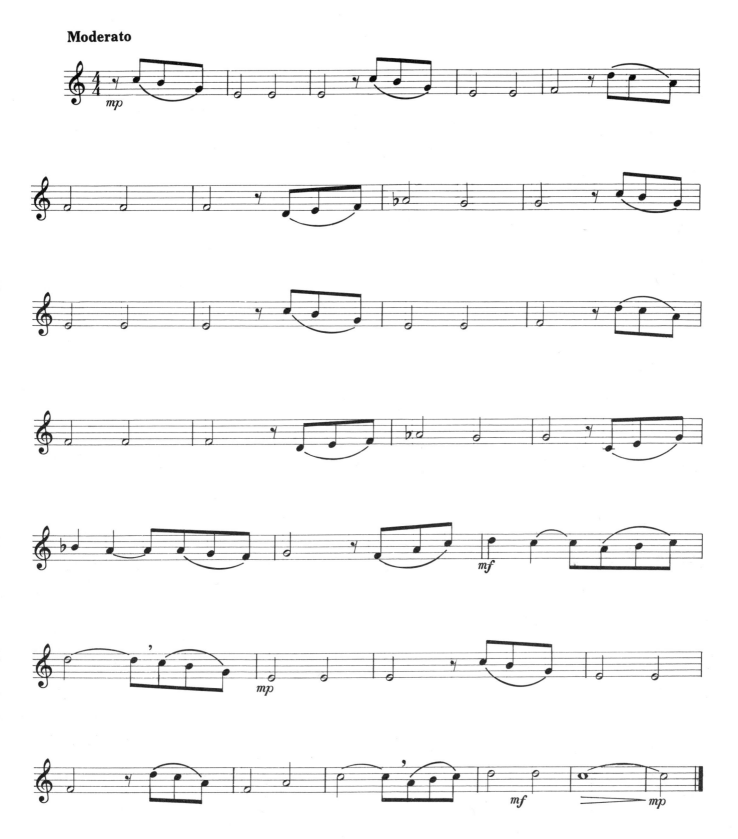

The Sound Of Silence.
Words and Music by Paul Simon.

Edelweiss.
Words by Oscar Hammerstein II. Music by Richard Rodgers.

Slowly, with expression

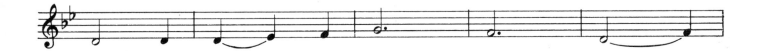

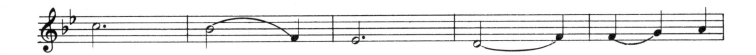

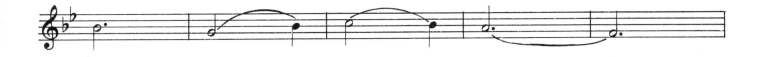

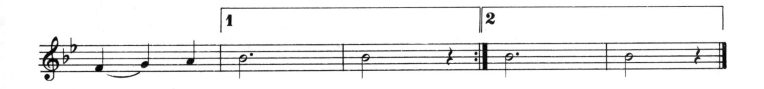

Chitty Chitty Bang Bang.
Words and Music by Richard M. Sherman and Robert B. Sherman.

A Man And A Woman (Un Homme Et Une Femme).

Music by Francis Lai. Original words by Pierre Barouh. English Lyric by Jerry Keller.

Hi-Lili, Hi-Lo.
Words by Helen Deutsch. Music by Bronislau Kaper.

Moderate waltz

High Noon.
Words by Ned Washington. Music by Dimitri Tiomkin.

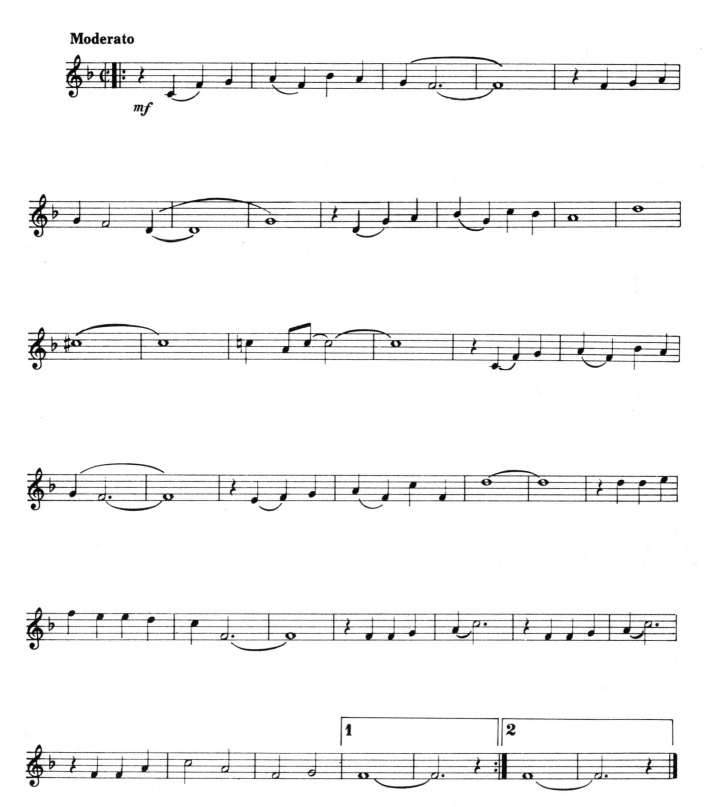

Sailing.
Words and Music by Gavin Sutherland.

Slow Beat

She's Leaving Home.
Words and Music by John Lennon & Paul McCartney.

Moderato

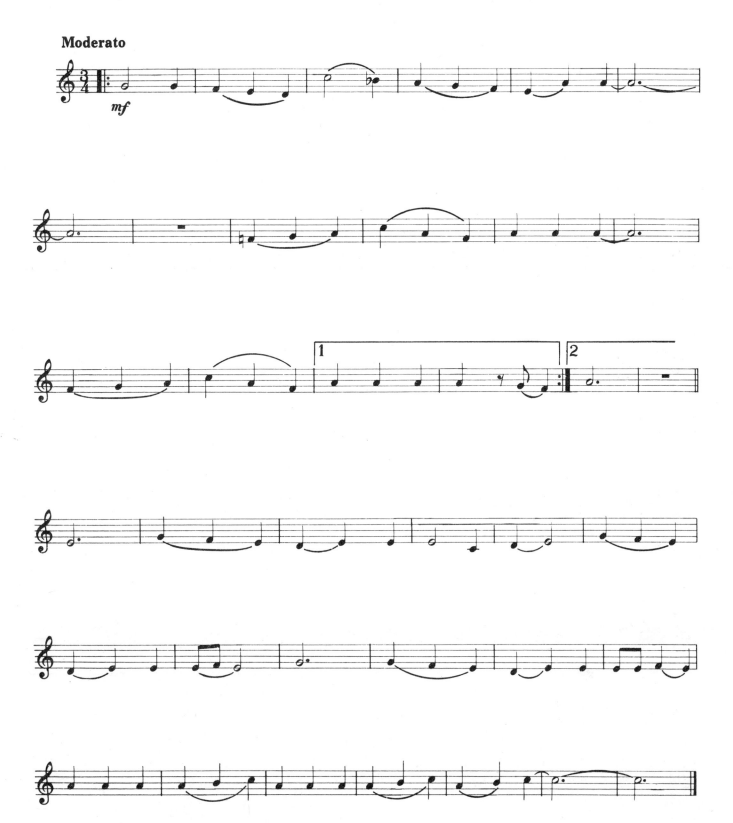

Love Me Tender.
Words and Music by Elvis Presley & Vera Matson.

Moderately slow

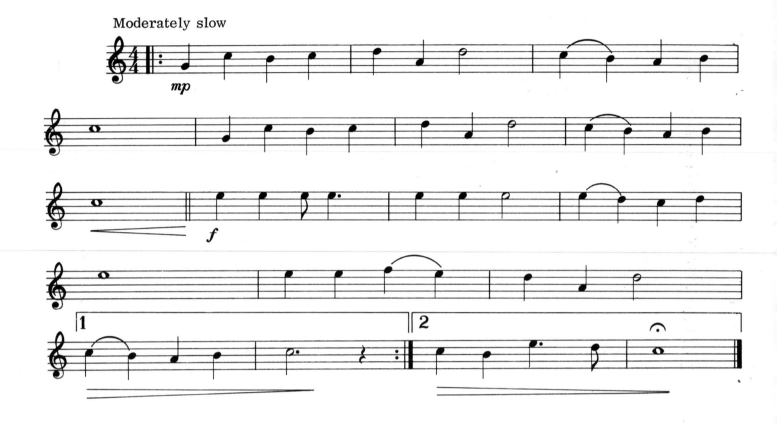

English Country Garden.
Words and Music by Robert M. Jordan.

Moderato

Be-Bop-A-Lula.
Words and Music by Gene Vincent & Sheriff Tex Davis.

Moderately slow rock

Chanson D'Amour.

Words and Music by Wayne Shanklin.

Medium rock tempo

Bring Me Sunshine.

Words by Sylvia Dee. Music by Arthur Kent.

With an easy swing

(Theme from) A Summer Place.
By Max Steiner.

Mona Bone Jakon.
Words and Music by Cat Stevens.

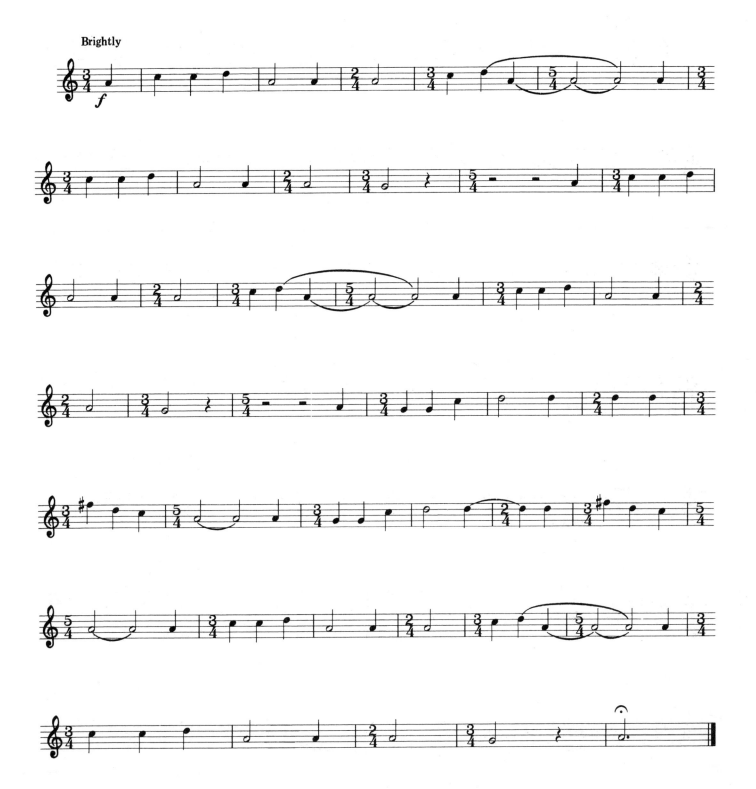

Over The Rainbow.

Words by E. Y. Harburg. Music by Harold Arlen.

Moderato

You Never Done It Like That.
Words by Howard Greenfield. Music by Neil Sedaka.

Scottish Dance
Beethoven

Moderately fast

Merry Dance
Rameau

Blue Suede Shoes.
Words and Music by Carl Lee Perkins.

Bright tempo

Cottonfields.
Words and Music by Huddie Ledbetter.

Birdie Song/Birdie Dance.
Words and Music by Werner Thomas & Terry Rendall.

I'd Like To Teach The World To Sing.

Words and Music by Roger Cook, Roger Greenaway, Billy Backer & Billy Davis.

Guantanamera.

Words by Jose Marti. Music adaptation by Hector Angulo & Pete Seeger.

Pick A Pocket Or Two.

Words and Music by Lionel Bart.

Never On Sunday.

Words by Billy Towne. Music by Manos Hadjidakis.

Jeanie With The Light Brown Hair
Stephen Foster

Moderato

Michelle.
Words and Music by John Lennon & Paul McCartney.

Moderato

How Can I Tell You.

Words and Music by Cat Stevens.

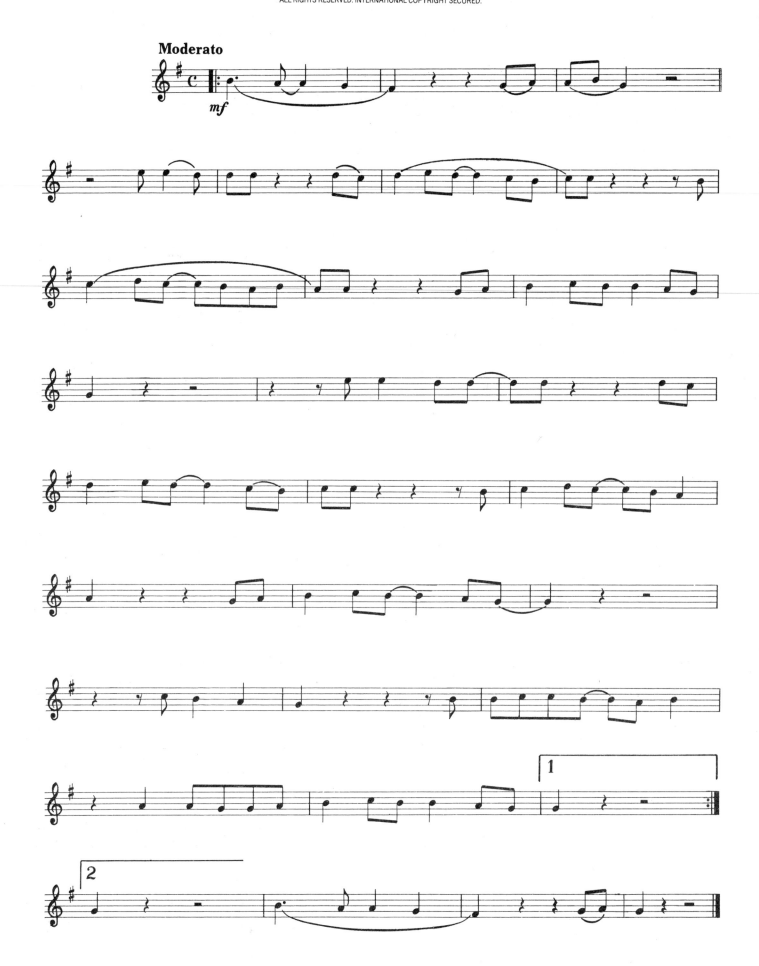

Steptoe And Son.
Music by Ron Grainer.

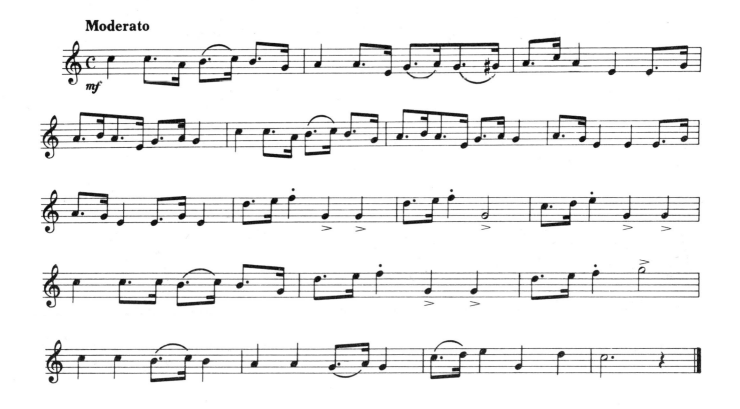

The Ballad of Davy Crockett.
Words by Tom Blackburn. Music by George Bruns.

Consider Yourself.
Words and Music by Lionel Bart.

Hawaii Five-O.
By Mort Stevens.

When I'm Sixty Four.
Words and Music by John Lennon & Paul McCartney.

Medium bounce

What Did You Learn In School Today.
Words and Music by Tom Paxton.

Slowly

Money, Money, Money.
Words and Music by Benny Andersson & Bjorn Ulvaeus.

Moderato

English Dance
J. C. Bach

Waltz
Brahms

Fairly slow

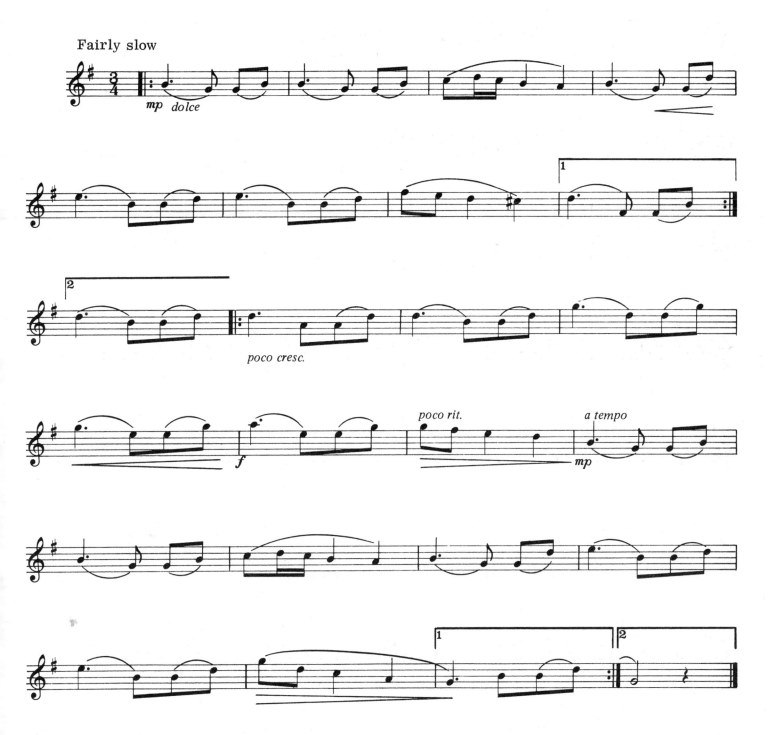

Where Is Love.
Words and Music by Lionel Bart.

Temptation.

Words by Arthur Freed. Music by Nacio Herb Brown.

Bibbidi-Bobbidi-Boo.
Words by Jerry Livingston. Music by Mack David & Al Hoffman.

Light Schottische tempo

What A Wonderful World.
Words and Music by George David Weiss & Bob Thiele.

White Rose Of Athens.

Music by Manos Hadjidakis. Words by Norman Newell. Additional words by Archie Bleyer.

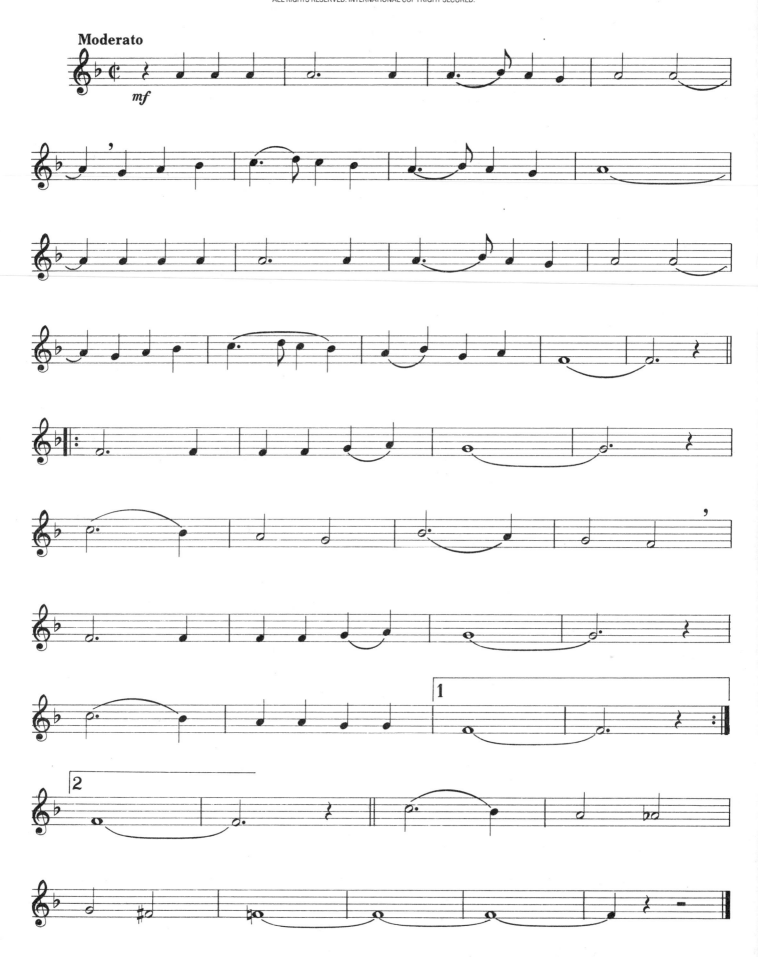

Annie's Song.
Words and Music by John Denver.

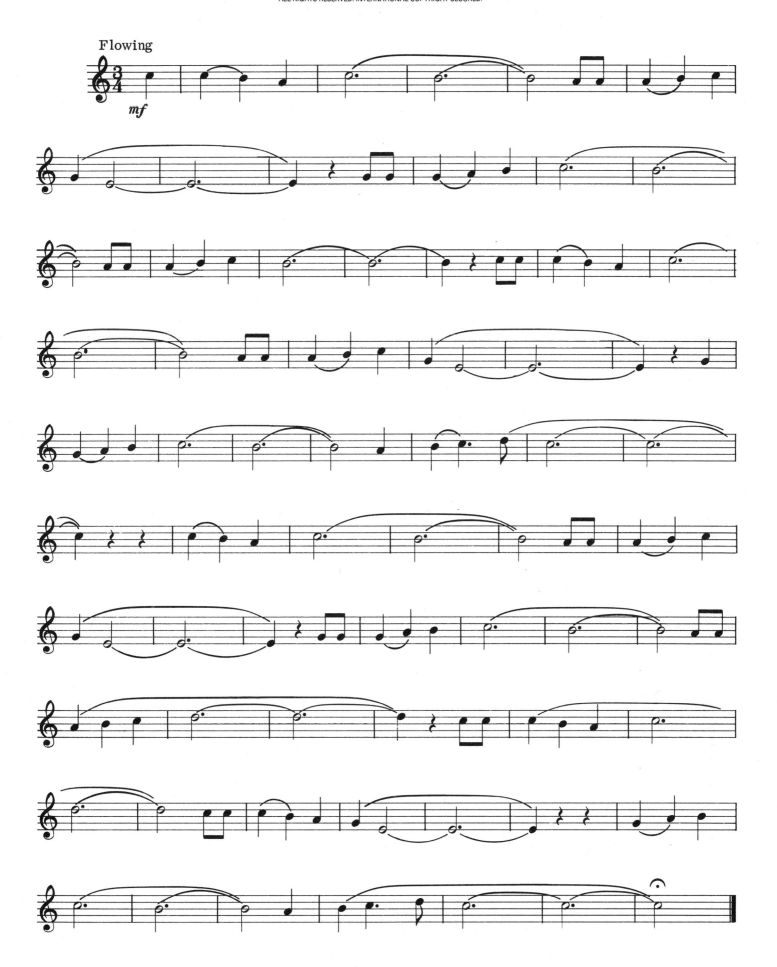

Who Will Buy.

Words and Music by Lionel Bart.

66

Imagine.
Words and Music by John Lennon.

Moderato

The Entertainer
Scott Joplin

Theme From Crossroads.
By Tony Hatch.

Strawberry Fields Forever.
Words and Music by John Lennon & Paul McCartney.

Reviewing The Situation.
Words and Music by Lionel Bart.

Norwegian Wood.

Words and Music by John Lennon & Paul McCartney.

Baby Love.

Words and Music by Brian Holland, Eddie Holland & Lamont Dozier.

Moonglow.

Words and Music by Will Hudson, Eddie De Lange & Irving Mills.

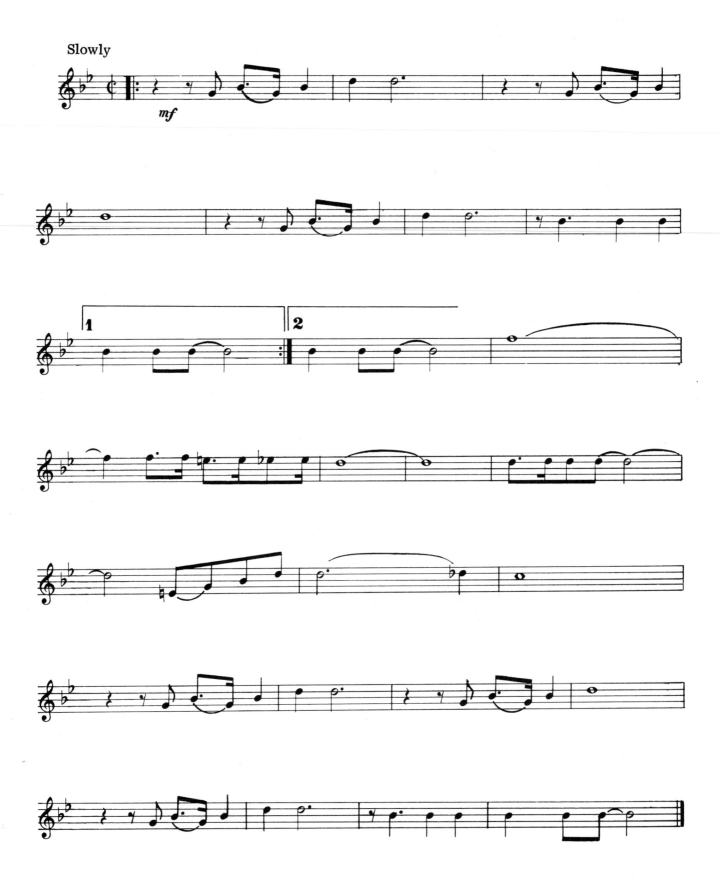

Oom Pah Pah.

Words and Music by Lionel Bart.

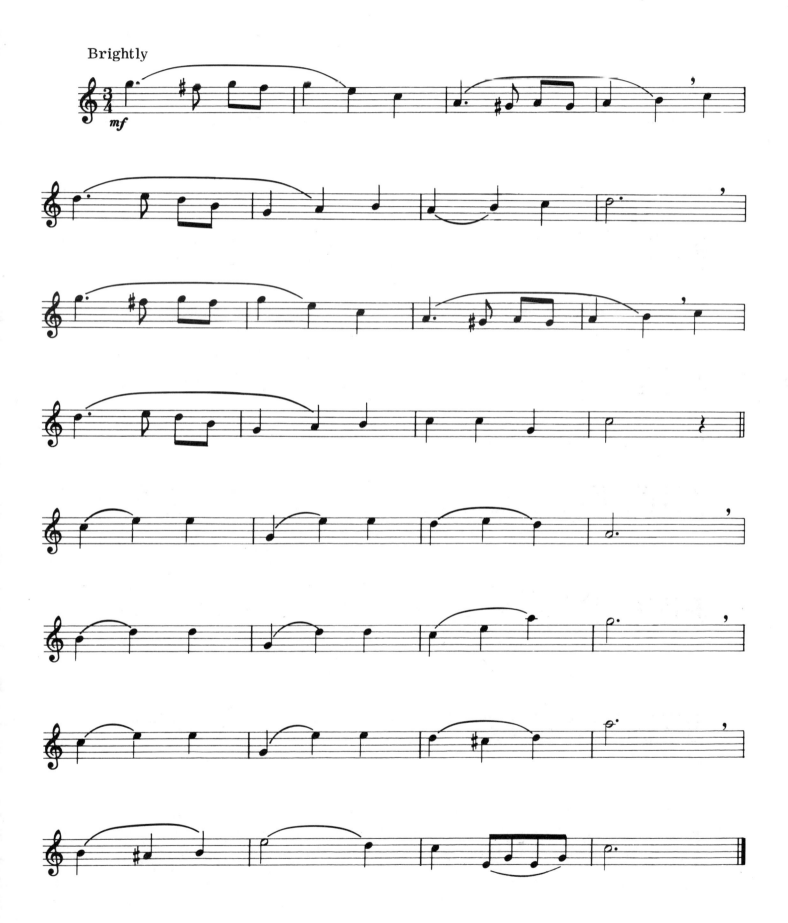

You're Nobody 'Til Somebody Loves You.
Words and Music by Russ Morgan, Larry Stock & James Cavanaugh.

When The Saints Go Marching In

Traditional

Top Of The World.

Words by John Bettis. Music by Richard Carpenter.

Yesterday Once More.
Words and Music by Richard Carpenter & John Bettis.

Repeat & fade.

The Girl From Ipanema (Garota De Ipanema).

Music by Antonio Carlos Jobim. Original words by Vinicius De Moraes. English lyric by Norman Gimbel.

Sgt. Pepper's Lonely Hearts Club Band.
Words and Music by John Lennon & Paul McCartney.

For All We Know.

Words by Robb Wilson & Arthur James. Music by Fred Karlin.

Moderato - with a light beat

Penny Lane.
Words and Music by John Lennon & Paul McCartney.

Moderately Bright

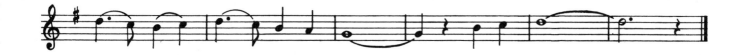

Lillywhite.
Words and Music by Cat Stevens.

Moderato

Bourée
Handel

Moderato

Carolina Moon.
Words by Benny Davis. Music by Joe Burke.

Valse moderato

Too Young.
Words by Sylvia Dee. Music by Sid Lippman.

Bluesette.
Words by Norman Gimbel. Music by Jean Thielemans.

Moderate waltz tempo

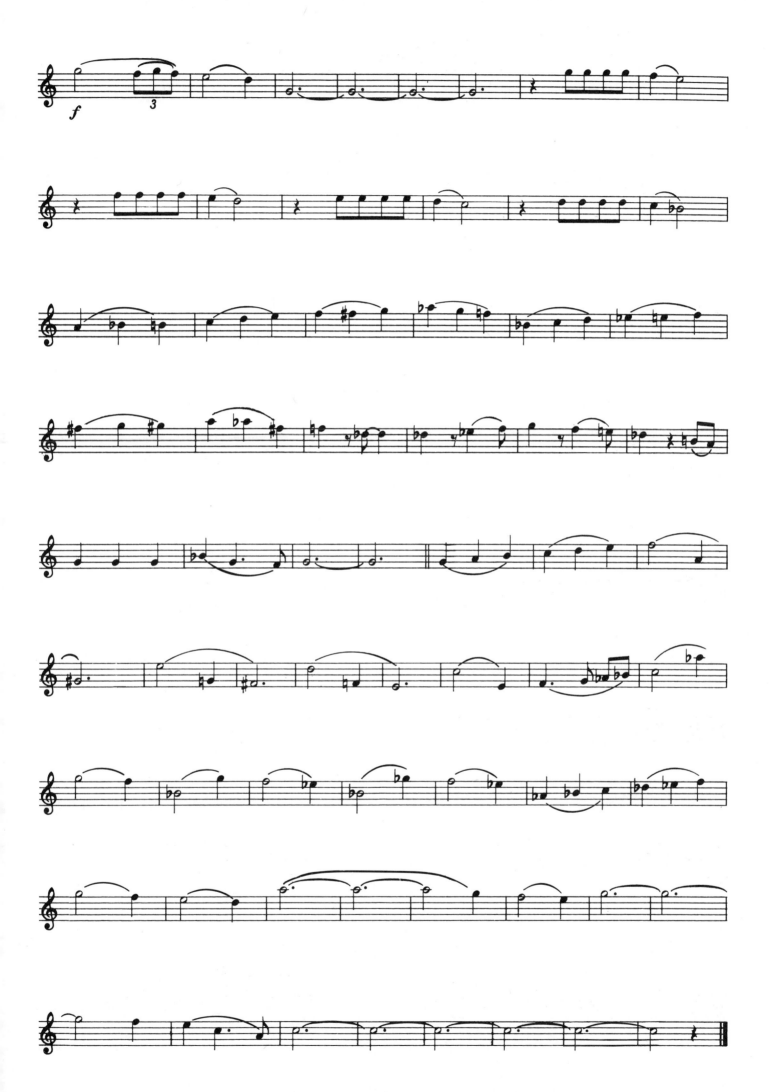

All Those Years Ago.
Words & Music by George Harrison.

All Shook Up.
Words and Music by Otis Blackwell & Elvis Presley.

Medium rock

Among My Souvenirs.
Words by Edgar Leslie. Music by Horatio Nicholls.

Moderato

Basin Street Blues.
Words and Music by Spencer Williams.

Moderato

With A Little Help From My Friends.

Words and Music by John Lennon & Paul McCartney.

Moderato

It's Not Unusual.

Words and Music by Gordon Mills & Les Reed.

Moderately, with a beat

Yellow Submarine.
Words and Music by John Lennon & Paul McCartney.

Moderately bright

3/86